Do You Remember?

M000188943

11 - 4	15 - 7	18 - 9
13 - 7	16 - 8	12 - 4	13 - 5
11 - 7	14 - 9	12 - 5	13 - 8
15 - 8	13 - 4	14 - 8	17 - 9
12 - 5	15 - 8	11 - 9	14 - 5

48 -26	66 -20	99 -41	65 -34
57 -14	89 -25	78 -30	99 -63
468 -135	396 -225	684 -452	789 -345
572 -460	864 -632	554 -131	526 -105

EMC 4065

Regroup to make one less set of tens.

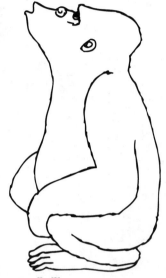

6 tens 5 ones = ___5___ tens ___15___ ones

9 tens 2 ones = ___8___ tens ___12___ ones

2 tens 7 ones = _____ ten _____ ones

8 tens 6 ones = _____ tens _____ ones

5 tens 8 ones = _____ tens _____ ones

6 tens 1 ones = _____ tens _____ ones

9 tens 4 ones = _____ tens _____ ones

7 tens 0 ones = _____ tens _____ ones

3 tens 3 ones = _____ tens _____ ones

Subtraction with Regrouping

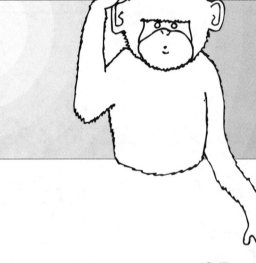

tens	ones
~~7~~	~~13~~
~~8~~	~~3~~
- 5	4
2	9

tens	ones
2	5
-	9

tens	ones
6	0
- 4	3

```
  92        56        85        48
- 73      - 19      - 47      -29
_____     _____     _____     _____


  76        57        63        80
- 28      - 28      - 46      - 33
_____     _____     _____     _____
```

EMC 4065

Subtraction with Regrouping

2 16	4 14		
3̸6̸	5̸4̸	82	43
- 7	- 7	- 4	- 9
29	47		

88	15	57	61
- 9	- 8	- 9	- 6

56	72	24	86
- 9	- 6	- 9	- 8

43	67	85	52
- 7	- 8	- 7	- 9

How do you know a gorilla was in your refrigerator?

18 - b   44 - h   78 - o   89 - s
56 - e   15 - i   63 - p   29 - t
36 - f   47 - n   27 - r   62 - u

³¹³ 4̶3̶ - 7	86 - 8	93 - 15	36 - 7
36			
f			

71 - 8	66 - 39	24 - 9	56 - 9	53 - 24	98 - 9

52 - 37	91 - 44

45 - 16	52 - 8	63 - 7

45 - 27	81 - 19	37 - 8	54 - 25	72 - 16	43 - 16

EMC 4065

Answer the problems.
Color the box brown if you had to regroup to help
the monkey reach the bananas.

2 11 3̸1̸ - 3 ——— 28	78 - 9	57 - 26	29 - 4
66 - 35	56 - 28	85 - 65	47 - 25
22 - 12	93 - 37	68 - 29	52 - 16

I can eat all of the fruit
with answers more than 50.

```
  5 14
   64
 - 28
 -----
   36
```

```
   97
 - 38
 -----
```

```
   56
 - 17
 -----
```

```
   85
 - 17
 -----
```

```
   93
 - 26
 -----
```

```
   38
 - 19
 -----
```

```
   46
 - 28
 -----
```

```
   50
 - 37
 -----
```

```
   94
 - 35
 -----
```

How many pieces of fruit do I get to eat? ☐

EMC 4065

Add to Check Subtraction

8 12 9̶2̶ - 15 77 77 +15 92	36 - 17
54 - 25	87 - 38
20 - 11	94 - 66
43 - 27	52 - 36

Tic-Tac-Toe

Put an X on problems where you had to regroup.
Put an O around problems with no regrouping.

56 - 42	37 - 14	55 - 28
62 - 31	81 - 66	84 - 21
98 - 49	96 - 34	37 - 13

Who won?
X or O

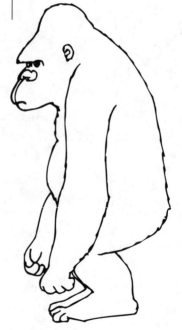

EMC 4065

Subtract

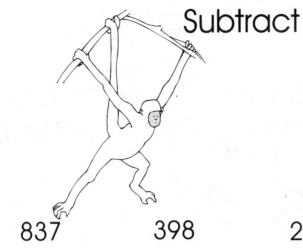

837 - 614 223	398 - 235	254 - 122	473 - 351
256 - 142	638 - 231	356 - 214	189 - 123
643 - 331	532 - 210	975 - 134	837 - 213
584 - 121	324 - 102	949 - 325	613 - 312

Add to Check Subtraction

$\overset{5\ 14}{3\cancel{6}\cancel{4}}$ $\overset{1}{3}26$ $-\ 38$ $+\ 38$ ──── ──── 326 364	488 $-\ 49$ ────
257 $-\ 28$ ────	625 $-\ 17$ ────
256 $-\ 29$ ────	964 $-\ 46$ ────
753 $-\ 39$ ────	571 $-\ 55$ ────

EMC 4065

Connect the dots in the order of the answers below.

135 218   249   347   526   147 148
●   ●   ●   ●   ●   ●   ●
● 249   ● 239
      519   ● 345
       ●   ● 218
      ●   ●   353
     307   127   ●

---

6 15				
~~275~~	388	682	456	491
- 127	-149	- 337	- 238	- 138
148				

236	824	765	678	262
- 109	- 517	- 246	- 429	- 127

346	378	695	842	386
- 128	- 129	- 348	- 316	- 239

Find the Difference

```
    15
  3 5 15
   465          826          783
 - 277        - 469        - 388
 _____       _____       _____
   188
```

```
   848          734          527
 - 179        - 157        - 489
 _____       _____       _____
```

```
   471          662          576
 - 186        - 275        - 289
 _____       _____       _____
```

```
   347          824          463
 - 198        - 267        - 379
 _____       _____       _____
```

EMC 4065

Solve these problems.
Color the coconuts brown
if you had to regroup.

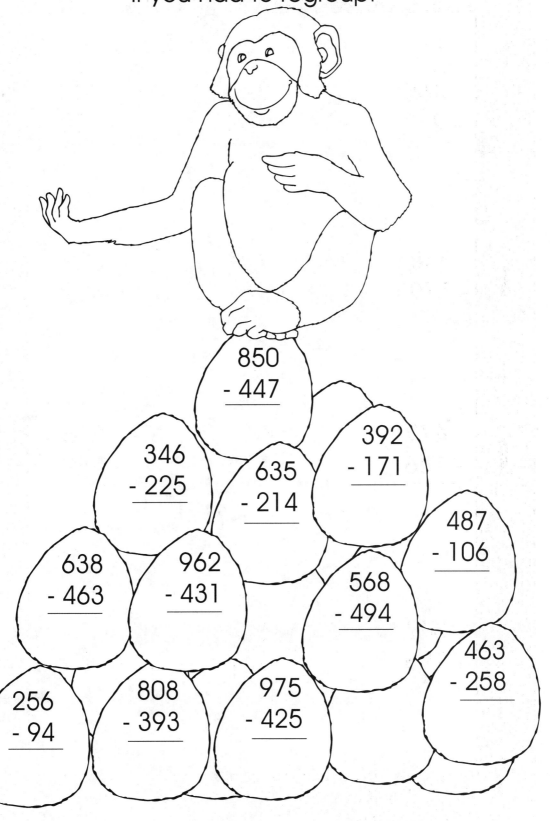

850
- 447
_____

346
- 225
_____

635
- 214
_____

392
- 171
_____

487
- 106
_____

638
- 463
_____

962
- 431
_____

568
- 494
_____

256
- 94
_____

808
- 393
_____

975
- 425
_____

463
- 258
_____

EMC 4065

Be careful with these.
You have to regroup two times.

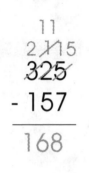

```
  11
 2 11 15
  3 2 5
-  1 5 7
---------
  1 6 8
```

```
  8 7 3
-  4 9 5
---------
```

```
  4 4 4
-  2 7 6
---------
```

```
  6 5 2
-  2 8 8
---------
```

```
  3 6 1
-  1 8 7
---------
```

```
  7 3 7
-  3 6 8
---------
```

```
  7 4 8
-    5 9
---------
```

```
  2 8 4
-  1 8 8
---------
```

```
  6 4 3
-  4 7 5
---------
```

EMC 4065

What is the difference?

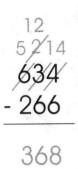

```
    12
  5 2 14
   6̶3̶4̶
 - 266
 ─────
   368
```

```
   432
 - 145
 ─────
```

```
   972
 - 694
 ─────
```

```
   546
 - 389
 ─────
```

```
   347
 - 168
 ─────
```

```
   524
 - 297
 ─────
```

```
   631
 - 463
 ─────
```

```
   426
 - 379
 ─────
```

```
   302
 - 148
 ─────
```

```
   456
 - 287
 ─────
```

```
   912
 - 667
 ─────
```

```
   356
 - 278
 ─────
```

These problems are wrong.
Find the mistakes and correct them.

```
  835          465
- 452        - 277
 ─────        ─────
  3̶9̶3̶          189
  383
```

```
  364          275          367
- 138         - 27        - 149
 ─────        ─────        ─────
  326          148          208
```

```
  254          837          584
- 122        - 213        - 221
 ─────        ─────        ─────
  122          514          463
```

```
  949          532          388
- 325        - 210        - 149
 ─────        ─────        ─────
  614          212          139
```

18

EMC 4065

Help this little monkey answer some riddles.

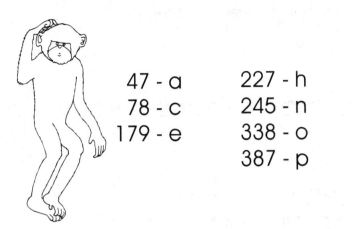

47 - a	227 - h	395 - r
78 - c	245 - n	427 - s
179 - e	338 - o	577 - t
	387 - p	

1. What has eyes but cannot see?

5 12 6̶6̶2̶ - 275	504 - 166	734 - 157	426 - 379	845 - 268	615 - 277
387					
p					

2. What has ears but cannot hear?

356 - 278	723 - 385	783 - 388	912 - 667

3. What has a tongue but cannot talk?

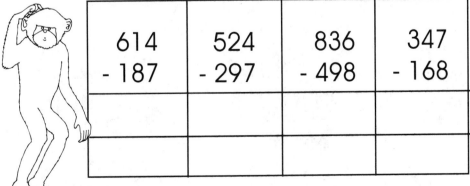

614 - 187	524 - 297	836 - 498	347 - 168

Help me find the answers to these problems.

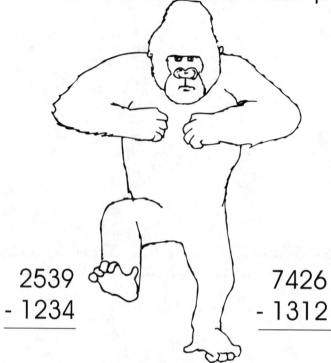

```
  2539              7426
- 1234            - 1312
_____            _____
```

```
  3748              7954              6395
- 1231            - 5123            - 2203
_____            _____            _____
```

```
  6389              9768              6854
- 4230            - 1422            - 1120
_____            _____            _____
```

```
  3287              8394              7945
- 1041            - 6023            - 1421
_____            _____            _____
```

EMC 4065

Look carefully to see where you have to regroup.

```
      214
   25314
  - 1229
  ------
   1305
```

```
      311
    74Y6
  - 1322
  ------
```

```
    9468
  - 1722
  ------
```

```
    6289
  - 3430
  ------
```

```
    6824
  - 3250
  ------
```

```
    3281
  - 1047
  ------
```

```
    8094
  - 6323
  ------
```

```
    7445
  - 3921
  ------
```

```
    7635
  - 4810
  ------
```

What side of an orangutan has the most hair?

2216 - d   1771 - h   2165 - s
1207 - e   4511 - i   2829 - t
3420 - g   1296 - o   1607 - u

5875 - 3046	4094 - 2323	2535 - 1328
2829		
t		

2539 - 1243	2963 - 1356	6268 - 3439

6845 - 4680	7334 - 2823	3263 - 1047	5473 - 4266

22

EMC 4065

Draw lines to match problems with the same answers.

6394
- 2918
___

5567
- 1643
___

2563
- 849
___

5841
- 2365
___

5831
- 1907
___

8371
- 6657
___

8586
- 1739
___

6062
- 938
___

6518
- 1394
___

9763
- 2916
___

Regroup Two Times

```
  11
7 X 16
 9826          6271          5432
-7377         -1454         -1806
─────         ─────         ─────
 2449


 2915          1482          8683
-1068          -954         -2194
─────         ─────         ─────


 8172          6831          7467
-2827         -1907         -1649
─────         ─────         ─────


 3714          8237          4652
-1907         -4652         -2919
─────         ─────         ─────
```

EMC 4065

Check Subtraction with Addition

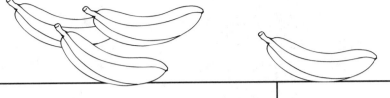

```
   3 16 2 12
    4̷6̷3̷2̷        2924
  - 1708       + 1708
  ──────       ──────
    2924         4632
```

```
    5215
  - 2166
  ──────
```

```
    9478
  - 2294
  ──────
```

```
    7685
  - 2827
  ──────
```

```
    7605
  - 4138
  ──────
```

```
    9253
  - 3618
  ──────
```

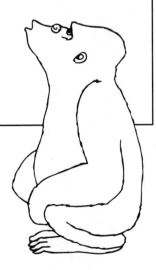

Subtraction Review

No regrouping

46 - 25	849 - 218	564 - 203	8438 - 5326

Regroup once

83 - 54	267 - 49	375 - 127	2534 - 1229

Regroup twice

465 - 277	325 - 157	620 - 359	6351 - 2846

EMC 4065

Take your time.

I know you
can do it.

Think as you work.

9351 - 2475	3124 - 2876	5823 - 2987
4625 - 2867	8543 - 4786	2528 - 1859
7987 -2998	9337 - 3659	5684 - 1786

EMC 4065

27

Solve these Problems

```
  4841          2623          9765
- 2876        - 1947        - 1876
_____        _____        _____
```

```
  6525          8528          5645
- 3758        - 2759        - 1978
_____        _____        _____
```

```
  7482          4953          6827
- 5686        - 3966        - 4978
_____        _____        _____
```

How many times did you have to regroup
in each problem?

28

Keep subtracting until
you reach the chimps.

6594	9904
- 1638	- 3657

4956	

| - 869 | - 3819 |

| - 2438 | - 760 |

| - 973 | - 894 |

| - 198 | - 296 |

Here are some challenges for you. Good luck!

3942801
- 1694736
_____

676869
- 398789
_____

987654321
- 123456789
_____

8000
- 2468
_____

How did you do?

111111111
- 96320651
_____

EMC 4065

Answer Key

Please take time to go over the work your child has completed. Ask your child to explain what he/she has done. Praise both success and effort. If mistakes have been made, explain what the answer should have been and how to find it. Let your child know that mistakes are a part of learning. The time you spend with your child helps let him/her know you feel learning is important.

page 1

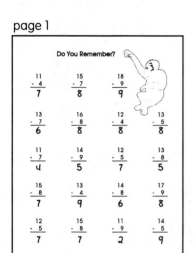

Do You Remember?

11 − 4 = **7**	15 − 7 = **8**	18 − 9 = **9**	
13 − 7 = **6**	16 − 8 = **8**	12 − 4 = **8**	13 − 5 = **8**
11 − 7 = **4**	14 − 9 = **5**	12 − 5 = **7**	13 − 8 = **5**
15 − 8 = **7**	13 − 4 = **9**	14 − 8 = **6**	17 − 9 = **8**
12 − 5 = **7**	15 − 8 = **7**	11 − 9 = **2**	14 − 5 = **9**

page 2

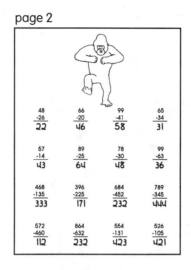

48 − 26 = **22**	66 − 20 = **46**	99 − 41 = **58**	65 − 34 = **31**
57 − 14 = **43**	89 − 25 = **64**	78 − 30 = **48**	99 − 63 = **36**
468 − 135 = **333**	396 − 225 = **171**	684 − 452 = **232**	789 − 345 = **444**
572 − 460 = **112**	864 − 632 = **232**	554 − 131 = **423**	526 − 105 = **421**

page 3

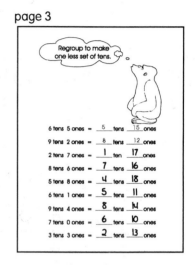

Regroup to make one less set of tens.

6 tens 5 ones = **5** tens **15** ones
9 tens 2 ones = **8** tens **12** ones
2 tens 7 ones = **1** ten **17** ones
8 tens 6 ones = **7** tens **16** ones
5 tens 8 ones = **4** tens **18** ones
6 tens 1 ones = **5** tens **11** ones
9 tens 4 ones = **8** tens **14** ones
7 tens 0 ones = **6** tens **10** ones
3 tens 3 ones = **2** tens **13** ones

page 4

Subtraction with Regrouping

tens ones	tens ones	tens ones
8 3 − 5 4 = **2 9**	2 5 − 9 = **1 6**	6 0 − 4 3 = **1 7**

92 − 73 = **19**	56 − 19 = **37**	85 − 47 = **38**	48 − 29 = **19**
76 − 28 = **48**	57 − 28 = **29**	63 − 46 = **17**	80 − 33 = **47**

page 5

Subtraction with Regrouping

36 − 7 = **29**	54 − 7 = **47**	82 − 4 = **78**	43 − 9 = **34**
88 − 9 = **79**	15 − 8 = **7**	57 − 9 = **48**	61 − 6 = **55**
56 − 9 = **47**	72 − 6 = **66**	24 − 9 = **15**	86 − 8 = **78**
43 − 7 = **36**	67 − 8 = **59**	85 − 7 = **78**	52 − 9 = **43**

page 6

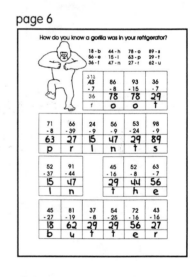

How do you know a gorilla was in your refrigerator?

18 - b   44 - h   78 - o   89 - s
56 - e   15 - i   63 - p   29 - t
36 - f   47 - n   27 - r   62 - u

43 − 7 = **36** f	86 − 8 = **78** o	93 − 15 = **78** o	36 − 7 = **29** t
71 − 8 = **63** p	66 − 39 = **27** r	24 − 9 = **15** i	56 − 9 = **47** n	53 − 24 = **29** t	98 − 9 = **89** s
52 − 37 = **15** i	91 − 44 = **47** n		45 − 16 = **29** t	52 − 8 = **44** h	63 − 7 = **56** e
45 − 27 = **18** b	81 − 19 = **62** u	37 − 8 = **29** t	54 − 25 = **29** t	72 − 16 = **56** e	43 − 16 = **27** r

page 7

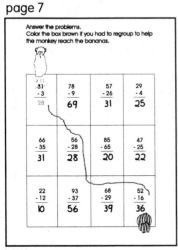

Answer the problems.
Color the box brown if you had to regroup to help the monkey reach the bananas.

31 − 3 = **28**	78 − 9 = **69**	57 − 26 = **31**	29 − 4 = **25**
66 − 35 = **31**	56 − 28 = **28**	85 − 65 = **20**	47 − 25 = **22**
22 − 12 = **10**	93 − 37 = **56**	68 − 29 = **39**	52 − 16 = **36**

page 8

I can eat all of the fruit with answers more than 50.

64 − 28 = **36**	97 − 38 = **59**	56 − 17 = **39**
85 − 17 = **68**	93 − 26 = **67**	38 − 19 = **19**
46 − 28 = **18**	50 − 37 = **13**	94 − 35 = **59**

How many pieces of fruit do I get to eat? **4**

page 9

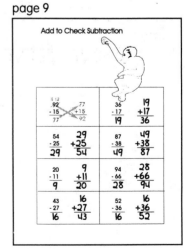

Add to Check Subtraction

92 − 15 = **77** / 77 + 15 = **92**	36 − 17 = **19** / 19 + 17 = **36**
54 − 25 = **29** / 29 + 25 = **54**	87 − 38 = **49** / 49 + 38 = **87**
20 − 11 = **9** / 9 + 11 = **20**	94 − 66 = **28** / 28 + 66 = **94**
43 − 27 = **16** / 16 + 27 = **43**	52 − 36 = **16** / 16 + 36 = **52**

page 10

Tic-Tac-Toe

Put an X on problems where you had to regroup.
Put an O around problems with no regrouping.

56 − 42 = 14 (O)	37 − 14 = 23 (O)	55 − 28 = 27 (X)
62 − 31 = 31 (O)	81 − 66 = 15 (X)	84 − 21 = 63 (O)
98 − 49 = 49 (X)	96 − 34 = 62 (O)	37 − 13 = 24 (O)

Who won? X or O

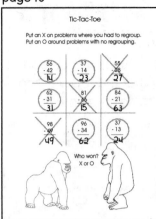

page 11

Subtract

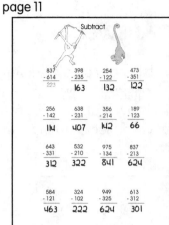

837 − 614 = 223	398 − 235 = 163	254 − 122 = 132	473 − 351 = 122
256 − 142 = 114	638 − 231 = 407	356 − 214 = 142	189 − 123 = 66
643 − 331 = 312	532 − 210 = 322	975 − 134 = 841	837 − 213 = 624
584 − 121 = 463	324 − 102 = 222	949 − 325 = 624	613 − 312 = 301

page 12

Add to Check Subtraction

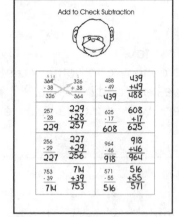

364 − 38 = 326	326 + 38 = 364	488 − 49 = 439	439 + 49 = 488
257 − 28 = 229	229 + 28 = 257	625 − 17 = 608	608 + 17 = 625
256 − 29 = 227	227 + 29 = 256	964 − 46 = 918	918 + 46 = 964
753 − 39 = 714	714 + 39 = 753	571 − 55 = 516	516 + 55 = 571

page 13

Connect the dots in the order
of the answers below.

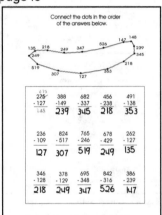

275 − 127 = 148	388 − 149 = 239	682 − 337 = 345	456 − 238 = 218	491 − 138 = 353
236 − 109 = 127	824 − 517 = 307	765 − 246 = 519	678 − 429 = 249	262 − 127 = 135
346 − 128 = 218	378 − 129 = 249	695 − 348 = 347	842 − 316 = 526	386 − 239 = 147

page 14

Find the Difference

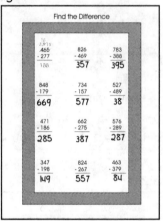

465 − 277 = 188	826 − 469 = 357	783 − 388 = 395
848 − 179 = 669	734 − 157 = 577	527 − 489 = 38
471 − 186 = 285	662 − 275 = 387	576 − 289 = 287
347 − 198 = 149	824 − 267 = 557	463 − 379 = 84

page 15

Solve these problems.
Color the coconuts brown
if you had to regroup.

850 − 447 = 403

346 − 225 = 121   635 − 214 = 421   392 − 171 = 221   487 − 106 = 381

638 − 463 = 175   962 − 431 = 531   568 − 494 = 74   463 − 258 = 205

256 − 94 = 162   808 − 393 = 415   975 − 425 = 550

page 16

Be careful with these.
You have to regroup two times.

325 − 157 = 168	873 − 495 = 378
444 − 276 = 168	652 − 288 = 364
361 − 187 = 174	737 − 368 = 369
748 − 59 = 689	284 − 188 = 96	643 − 475 = 168

page 17

What is the difference?

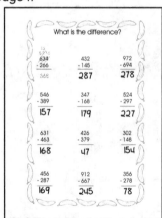

634 − 266 = 368	432 − 145 = 287	972 − 694 = 278
546 − 389 = 157	347 − 168 = 179	524 − 297 = 227
631 − 463 = 168	426 − 379 = 47	302 − 148 = 154
456 − 287 = 169	912 − 667 = 245	356 − 278 = 78

page 18

These problems are wrong.
Find the mistakes and correct them.

835 − 452 = 383	465 − 277 = 188	
364 − 138 = 226	275 − 27 = 248	367 − 149 = 218
254 − 122 = 132	837 − 213 = 624	584 − 221 = 363
949 − 325 = 624	532 − 210 = 322	388 − 149 = 239

page 19

Help this little monkey answer some riddles.

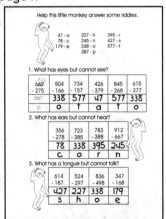

47 - a   227 - h   395 - r
78 - c   245 - n   427 - s
179 - e   338 - o   577 - t
          387 - p

1. What has eyes but cannot see?

662 − 275 = 387	504 − 166 = 338	734 − 157 = 577	426 − 379 = 47	845 − 268 = 577	615 − 277 = 338
p	o	t	a	t	o

2. What has ears but cannot hear?

356 − 278 = 78	723 − 385 = 338	783 − 388 = 395	912 − 667 = 245
c	o	r	n

3. What has a tongue but cannot talk?

614 − 187 = 427	524 − 297 = 227	836 − 498 = 338	347 − 168 = 179
s	h	o	e

page 20

Help me find the answers to these problems.

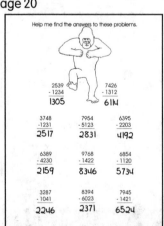

2539 − 1234 = 1305	7426 − 1312 = 6114
3748 − 1231 = 2517	7954 − 5123 = 2831	6395 − 2203 = 4192
6389 − 4230 = 2159	9768 − 1422 = 8346	6854 − 1120 = 5734
3287 − 1041 = 2246	8394 − 6023 = 2371	7945 − 1421 = 6524

page 21

Look carefully to see where you have to regroup.

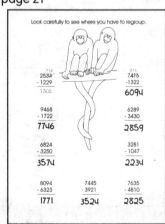

2534 − 1229 = 1305	7416 − 1322 = 6094
9468 − 1722 = 7746	6289 − 3430 = 2859
6824 − 3250 = 3574	3281 − 1047 = 2234
8094 − 6323 = 1771	7445 − 3921 = 3524	7635 − 4810 = 2825

EMC 4065